The Wisdom of Fionn

Waterford City and County
Libraries

Fergus Hogan

WestWay, Rockfield, Athenry,
Co. Galway, Ireland.
www.bookhubpublishing.com

@BookHubPublish

Ilustrator: Frank Sammon
Designer: Lacey O'Connor
Editor: Niall McElwee

ISBN: 978-0-9932256-4-2

Acknowledgements

Like everything in life this book would not be possible but for the inspiration and loving encouragement of many. I have been blessed to share this journey with some wonderful teachers, mentors, friends and guides. Whether they hear the echo of their care and wisdom in these pages I wish to honour some of them.

Imelda McCarthy has always been an inspiration. Her re-awakening of *The Fifth Province* as a "healing space within" is something sacred and is the heart of this book. Together with Jim Sheehan they introduced me to the therapeutic power of narrative - that *Once Upon a Time, Words were Magic.* Harry Ferguson opened doors to the beauty of being with men in groups and social work practice where we realised the truth that behind anger is sadness, and where we re-discovered the healing power of Love. While Colm O'Connor the Poet Therapist shared the *Courage to be Happy and The Courage to Love.*

The wisdom of other authors is also present here. Ben Okri, the great Nigerian Poet and Booker Prize winning novelist says we are *Homo Fabula* – Storytelling Beings – that all we ever are is the stories we tell about ourselves. Stories that have been told float in the air all around us till they fall to the land where they seep into the stones and the bones of our being. The great Irish storyteller, mystic and philosopher John Moriarty reminds us that we dream ourselves into being and that at times we find ourselves in a field of sadness and the sadness is not of our making. Thomas Moore - the beautiful Soul Therapist of our times - invites us to remember such things as the ancient word for depression is melancholy, and the cure for melancholy is to be by water. While Michael Meade, the American mythopoeic storyteller, recognises the importance for us to live by fire as well as water.

I want to acknowledge with love the brotherhood and Sacred Masculine energy of the Campfire Storytellers; Ken, Darragh, Roland, Art, Diarmuid and Vispi; together with the Divine Feminine energy of the Shamanic Circle; Claire, Lolly, Karen, Rose, Pema and Roma.

Warm thanks to: Kathy McKay and Magda Lipinska who proof read and reviewed this work – the gift of their kindness is present in the punctuation; Maurits Wysmans was there at the start of the re-telling of this tale and has been a constant encouragement; Lonán Hogan was the first to read the finished piece; and my publisher Niall for making it real.

My special thanks and love to Irena Loveikaite.

Contents

Introduction

O nce upon a time, a long time ago, in a time before time, there was a very special time that was at the very centre of the world. That time still beats in the very heart of each and every one of us.

At that time a very special child was born - Fionn mac Cumhaill. He was to become one of the greatest, strongest, wisest, and gentlest of men ever to live in the lands of Ireland. His name became known throughout the land and his company was prized among others. You might think that the story of becoming such a wise and wonderful person would be a tale filled simply with triumph and joy. But, each of us knows that being born to become the wonderful person we are does not lead to an easy life. In all lives, we are faced with times of sadness and loss, fear and terror, as well as being touched with occasions of joy and love.

Fionn's journey through the life he was born into is no different in that way from yours or mine. His life journey to become his true self was filled with danger and risk, and times facing decisions and making choices that would affect not just his own life, but also the world around him.

For all of us, our lives are made up of the choices we make: choices we cannot avoid no matter how hard or painful they may seem at the time. The struggle of life is to try to live the life we have been given in the best way we can.

Making the wrong choice can lead us down a path that brings pain and suffering. The right choices lead us back to the true path of happiness in our life, our Soul's Path: the path that leads towards the destiny of who we were born to be.

Like many children born into this world, Fionn was born to parents who did not raise him, one parent who could not, the other who chose not to. Fionn spent his early years being raised in the care of two of his Aunts, Bovmall and Lia Luachra. Some might think this strange, but, strange as it may be to them, this is the very place that this story begins...

IMBOLC

Living in the Rhythm of Nature

~e~

F ionn was the son of Uail, the chief of the Fianna of Ireland, one of the greatest and most feared armies on the land of Ireland at the time. His mother was the beautiful Muirne who named her son Fionn, but she did not raise her son herself because she is said to have lived in fear of his safety. The story tells that, a short time before Fionn was born the rogues of the clan-Morna killed his father, Uail, in battle. It was one of the most savage killings ever seen or heard of in Ireland and when Muirne gave birth to a son of Uail's she gave him into the care of Uail's sisters, Bovmall and Lia Luachra. She asked that they would raise Fionn in the safety of the forest. Legend says she gave her son over to their care with many more warnings and notices of how they should care for him in her absence. Others say Muirne gave her son into the care of his Aunts not because she loved him and feared for his life but because she had fallen in love with the King of Kerry.

It might be very hard to imagine for most, but Fionn lived with his Aunts in a world and a time before electric lights, or radio, or television. A time long before computer games and the Internet! Fionn's Aunts raised him well: some would even say they loved him. When he fell they lifted him; when he bruised his leg, they would rub it, for him, with healing herbs from the forest. However, word also went round that the Aunts also treated him hard and cruel sometimes. People said they taught him to swim, by dropping him into the deepest well in the woods and walking away leaving him to find his own way out. They taught him to run: some would say with abuse, by chasing him around an oak tree holding a hazel switch in their hands and when they caught him, he felt the sting of the switch. They taught him speed and agility by making him herd hares in fields with no hedges. But by a young age, Fionn could run as fast as any hare in the fields or the forest and swim as swiftly as the fish in the ponds and rivers.

Growing up with his Aunts in the countryside, Fionn spent most of his time outdoors, living and playing and growing alongside nature. From the youngest of ages, Fionn understood the rhythm of the world, that day followed night, just as winter came before the spring. Fionn understood that each season had its time and reason. Fionn learned to trust that time would heal all pains and that Nature was something that we could all benefit more from the closer we lived our lives, as his Aunt's always said: "in accordance with God's will."

His Aunts had taught Fionn that we are all part of the world: that we share our time on this planet with all living creatures. This natural sharing and living in the world together taught Fionn a respect for himself and others. And a deep belief in taking care of the world so as to be able to pass on God's gifts to the next generation of children. His Aunts had a saying: "We must respect the world around us because we have only borrowed it from our children."

Fionn knew that the Earth would always provide all that we need in order to feed ourselves, and to heat our homes, and to keep us safe.

And that all we need to do in life is learn how to share our world with each other.

Fionn grew up with his Aunts never eating meat – they never killed an animal in order to feed themselves. Fionn never thought strange of this as there was always enough food provided by the world. One day though he asked his Aunts why they never ate meat as there were so many rabbits in the fields and fish in the lakes: "Surely we could eat a few?" he suggested.

As always, his Aunts were keen to answer and so teach Fionn, and, while his Aunts never quite disagreed in their advice, each of them always had words of wisdom of their own to impart. Usually Bovmall was the first to speak.

"Well, just because you are able to do something in life, doesn't always mean it is the right thing to do. Every choice you make in life has an effect, not just for you, but also in the world around you. You could choose to eat meat here and that choice would have an effect on another person somewhere on the other side of the world."

"I cannot understand that," replied Fionn.

"Well," said Lia Luachra, "The earth is a small world and there are very many people trying to live off the resources of the world. Throughout the world there are people starving, children going hungry, dying even, because of choices made in other parts of the world. Even though the world is small, it is big enough to grow enough vegetables and cereal crops, rice and maize, to feed every living person. But the world is not big enough to produce enough meat to allow all people to eat it. Choosing to eat meat in one part of the world means other people will go hungry."

Bovmall could still see the quizzical look on Fionn's face, "In some ways it is very simple Fionn. Everyone and everything in this world is connected, even though we cannot always see the connections with our eyes. But we can always feel the connections with our heart. If we eat the rabbits in the forest, the fox cubs will go hungry and die. If there are not enough foxes in the forest, then there will be too many rabbits and rats the next year, and they will eat all the grain and wheat, and then we will not be able to make flour and bread. So you see, we are all connected and living in a hidden type of balance, the insects, the flowers, the birds, the animals, the fish and people too. We all depend on each other to help make the world go round."

Fionn began to make some sense of what they were saying, "So the decisions I make in life are important to the world as well as to my own life?" His Aunts became excited with the conversation. Lia Luachra smiled and spoke: "You cannot live your life outside of the world but always connected with each other. It is the same kind of thing with our decisions about how we share the energy resources of the world, how we share healing herbs and medicine, love and respect with all of the people of the world."

Then Bovmall warned: "You must be very careful with the choices you make in life, Fionn. You cannot live life without facing decisions - to live means making choices and each choice brings you to a different place. Choices are very special things - they have the power to do good or evil."

"I do not understand" said Fionn.

"Well," said Bovmall warmly, "you will be faced with a certain number of choices everyday. The choices you face today are based on the decisions you made yesterday. If you had made different decisions yesterday, you would face different choices today. The choices you make today will influence the decisions you will have to face tomorrow."

"Your life depends on having the courage to make choices" replied Lia Luachra.

The messages that his Aunts were passing on to Fionn seemed to be very important to him and he thought quietly to himself for a moment, "How can I be sure of always making the right choices in life?"

His Aunts seemed to even hear his thoughts. "You cannot always be sure. All you can do is try and live your life doing the best that you can, even when this means making difficult decisions."

"An Emotional Warrior always accepts the challenge of making a decision." "Yes, but how will I know?" asked Fionn. His Aunts smiled and then spoke softly, "There are two guiding principles in life that can help you. Do unto others, as you would have them do unto you."

"And, always believe in yourself."

Fireside Stories

~e2~

I n the evenings, they sat around the open fire telling stories. It was Fionn's job to gather enough firewood each day for the evening fire. When the fire burnt out, the light would be gone and it was then time to sleep. This was the way of the world at that time.

Even from the earliest of years, Fionn knew where to look for the best types of firewood. Wood that was good to start the fire at first, then wood to build up the fire, wood for slow burning and long stories, and woods with special scents which changed the mood of the house and company.

In all his time of gathering wood for the fire, Fionn never ever cut down a tree. Once Fionn had heard a warning: "never cut down a tree without planting one." He knew that to do so would be to go against one of the orders of nature. The Earth would always provide without the need to do damage. And it always did - the storm winds knew which of the older dangerous trees to blow down and, when they did fall, the branches shattered, breaking into smaller, more manageable sizes - just right for burning in the right company.

At night, just before the last of the day's good light was gone, Fionn's Aunts would take turns starting the fire. Fionn did not know if this was real or magic, but there always seemed to be enough warmth left in the hearth from the night before to start the fire again.

A good fire is like a good story: neither goes out and you have to watch both of them in case they catch you off guard. Once the fire was lit, his Aunts would almost sit in on top of the fire itself. So close, it was not clear if they were keeping the fire company or the other way round. They could sit for hours, for days even, and say nothing at all. Just being together, no words. From time to time one word, strong words: Just; Faith; A Stór. Then the other would nod, and they would both disappear back into the comfort of silence. For these two women had reached a time in their life where silence and stillness held no fear for them.

Fionn was different. He was younger; he wanted adventure and action; he wanted to know all there was to know about the past, the present, and the future. Fionn was like all youngsters, he was in a hurry to understand the world, everything. So he loved when he could encourage his Aunts to tell stories that they were so good at telling and which they never seemed to run out of. This was the other thing his Aunts did in the evening time before television - they told stories.

As usual Bovmall began, "Stories are very special things, indeed. Stories connect people, places, and times. Stories tell us all we have in common. Stories bring us to different places; all we have to do is listen. Stories connect us in time, remembering our past, present, and future. Stories are told together to bridge differences, to heal wounds, to comfort and care. There is an old saying that when the bond between Heaven and Earth is broken, even a prayer can't fix it, only a story will do."

It made sense to Fionn because he knew the healing power of stories. Often at times when he was hurt, or lonely, or scared, he would turn to one of his Aunts and ask them to tell him a story. Their stories helped to make him feel safe again.

Not to be out done, Lia Luachre spoke up too, "Stories are also told to teach, to forewarn the future, of people and situations, of the risks, the challenges, and the changes you will have to meet as you travel through life. You should always listen to a story very carefully because you will always need the wisdom of that story at sometime in the future. If you have not learned how to listen completely, you will be lost. You will miss your chance and will have to wait until both the story and the time come to you again. That is what they mean when they say, 'some people never seem to learn'."

The Seanachaí

I n olden times in Ireland, some very special people were gifted with the power of telling stories. These people, the 'Seanachaí,' travelled the land, never choosing to live for very long in the one place or time. They visited different places and offered stories in return for food, shelter and good company.

It is said that if you did not offer good food, or shelter, or company, the travelling storyteller would move on to another place and time. The storyteller would then pass on a story with a curse, which would tell of those who had closed the door of welcome in their face. Many people know what it is like to have a curse of a Seanachaí put on them. False words can cut in two ways. The first damage they do is when they are heard and believed to begin with. The second damage they do is when people try to deny the rumour! People always say, "there you go, it must be true, look at how he tries to deny it."

To give a warm welcome, and offer to share what you had in your home by way of food, shelter, and good company, brought the promise of a story that would reach to all corners of the county: a story that sang your praises and offered kindness to your children, and to your children's children, for generations to come.

These travelling storytellers made their living trading in such stories, words of poetry and curses. The curse of a Seanachaí needs a very special anti-spell to lift the curse and restore the person's good name. Seanachaís held the power of the story, either to praise or to curse. And so legend has it that Ireland is the place where the two sides of the story began!

Seanachaís were also among the wisest poets in the land. They knew the true potential of words. They knew that words were originally magic. That, in the beginning, all there was, was the Word. They knew that to choose one word over another would change the course of history. They knew what word to give to save, or curse, or help each person that asked. Legend has it that when the Seanachaís were down on their luck, they would, at times, sell words: special words, healing words.

One of the most beautiful of poets in the land once said - "Whatever you say - say nothing" - his wisdom warning of the power that words have to cause hurt and damage. A warning that, if you do not have something positive to say about someone, say nothing! The advice has taken deep roots in Ireland where many are afraid to say anything critical or negative about another for fear that bad luck will come back and haunt them.

Fionn's Aunts always warned against this myth, "Many people fear the truth in their own voice. They expect others to speak for them, or to speak more clearly. They fear the wisdom of their own beliefs or intuition so they remain silent. Most of all people fall silent in the face of danger, risk, and evil. To say nothing at these times is as bad as actually agreeing with the evil that is being done. Everyone has been given a voice, a way of communicating with the Soul, a way of speaking good, of speaking against evil. Never fear the truth of your own voice. Speak clearly and loudly for what you believe to be good and truthful. Never remain silent in the hope of protecting the feelings of another always, speak out. Say something, even if it is just to voice your intentions. The worst that can happen, when you speak out loud, is that you realise you have made a mistake in the way you said something. Never be afraid to apologise."

"Decide to think with your heart, and speak through your heart, and speak from your Soul. Then your word will truly become magical and healing. The story you tell in life about yourself and others is very important. Choose your words carefully. Never underestimate yourself and do not disrespect others. Stories, once they have been told, stay in the air, until a time when they fall and live on the ground until a time when they sink into the very stones of the earth and the bones of people's bodies."

Stories, Dreams and Imagination

~e2~

Stories are very special indeed. They are one of the three things in life that connect time: the past, the present and the future.

"What are the other two things that connect across the past, the present and the future?" wondered Fionn.

"Dreams" answered Bovmall.

"And Imagination," whispered Lia Luachra.

"Your dreams," Bovmall explained, "can bring you back to a time in the past or forward to your future, like your imagination and stories do also. When you dream, you should never be afraid. Not even when your dreams seem to scare you."

"Go on," said Fionn, "tell me some more."

"Well - sometimes we dream of times past; a time, for example, when we were hurt or upset or scared. These dreams have a habit of repeating themselves: we have them over and over like a nightmare that wakes us at the same point in the dream each night! Do you understand?"

"Yes"

"Usually at a time when we are most scared, and in trouble in the dream, when we are surrounded by mysterious shadows and with a sense of fear, we awake, frightened, sweaty, crying out in the night. But if we chose to stay asleep, to stay in the dream, we would be able to see the next part of the dream. The part that teaches us how we got out of the trouble, what we did next in order to survive."

Lia Luachra interrupted, "You see, Fionn, if we remember something, even something that was terrible in our lives, it means that we have lived to tell the tale. We have survived. Everyone who breathes, and wakes, and dreams, and remembers, is a survivor. We usually wake just before the answer to our questions is given to us through our dreams. Nightmares from the past just prove that we are the heroes in own lives."

Fionn was thinking about it, "How do dreams connect with the future?" he wondered.

"Well - have you ever found yourself doing something and suddenly thinking to yourself, I was here before. I did this, or said this, exactly like this before? Well, the reason you feel like this is because you dreamt about it. You just forgot your dream."

"Before you go to sleep you should decide to try to remember your dreams when you wake. Sometimes, it's hard to make sense of your dreams, so you might write them down - the characters in the dream, the place, the colour, the feelings, the music, the temperature. But remember, while others can help you talk about your dreams, only one person can decide what your dreams actually mean to you. That's you."

"Dreams help to warn you what is about to happen in your life, who you might meet and how you might need to react to them. For example, if you meet someone in your dream and you feel angry or you shout at them, then you might need to learn how to get angry with that person in your own life. Or, if you feel sorry and sad, you might benefit from offering them an apology or telling them how you really feel about them."

"Sometimes you can dream about someone you need or want

to meet again, and then find yourself bumping into them soon afterwards."

"What about day dreams?" Fionn loved daydreams and his Aunts never gave out to him for getting distracted!

"They are the same. They bring us places we need to go; they help remind us of people we have forgotten or places we might not even have visited yet!"

"Children know the healing power of day dreams, yet too often adults tell children to wake up - to stop day dreaming! We shatter dreams by saying 'that was just a dream'."

Fionn thought to himself, "The healing power of day dreams?" And, as had often happened before Bovmall seemed to know what he was thinking.

"Yes, of course. Have you ever watched the look on a child's face as their eyes follow a butterfly, or a cloud, or a cat chase its own shadow?"

"Yes"

"Well, that is the look of magic, that's the moment you can see magic: The look on someone's face when they have just drifted off into a daydream - that is real magic. You know, it is a wonderful thing when you call them and call them and they still can not hear you, they are lost in the beauty of their imagination."

Lia Luachre joined in, "Imagination is healing too, but we teach children to forget that also."

Fionn was struggling to keep up with all of the ideas, "I really do not understand now."

Lia Luachra smiled like she had just had a magical day dream herself, "Well, remember when you were small, and when you would fall and cut your knee, and you thought it hurt you so much it made you cry? And then one of us would kiss it better and make all the pain go away, and we would sprinkle some magic healing dust onto your knee and it would speed up the healing process?"

Fionn smiled too, as he warmly remembered the times, "Of course I remember."

"Well, it really worked, and that is the healing power of imagination - and that is what we teach children to forget. We tell them to grow up and not to be silly; we teach them the magic dust is not really real. And then children forget to believe in healing and the healing power of imagination."

"I think I need another example."

"Well, a sad example is when a doctor tells a patient that they are really sick and that they are going to die. If the patient is older and has lost faith in the healing power of imagination, they suddenly begin to feel worse and worse and often they give up all hope of living. Dying becomes so much easier than living because they believe there is nothing left to live for. When the patient is younger - some say when they do not understand; others say when the child still believes in faith, and hope, and prayer, and imagination - the possibilities that life offers are unending. Often that child simply does not listen to the prediction that they 'should die.' Sometimes the child dies, but, even if they die, it usually takes longer than the doctors expected, because the child lived life till the end, rather than just giving up. But also often, the child, that medical experts said should die, simply believed in the healing power of imagination. They could not die because they had not yet lived all they had imagined possible for themselves."

"That's what the experts call miracles after they have been proven wrong" answered Bovmall.

While Lia Luachra continued, "Always believe in yourself. Your dreams can become true. Your dreams are one of the best places to see the truth of who we were born to be. When we imagine who we want to be, we make certain choices to help us get there."

Fionn was beginning to understand more clearly, "So, dreams and imagination and choices are all connected. But how will I know if I am living the best life possible?"

"There are two things to remember. Firstly, in life you can make choices that allow your greatest dreams to to come true" smiled Lia Luachra.

"And secondly, we are happiest in life when we follow the path that is closest to our imagination," beamed Bovmall.

Prayer and Meditation

As they talked by the dancing firelight, Fionn began to feel sleepy. He seemed to drift in and out of sleep; he was not sure if his Aunts were still talking with him, or if he was just imagining them still in his dreams. Their words were strong yet gentle. They whispered to him about prayers and meditation. He smiled in his sleep.

"Never fear your dreams. Use them to help you become the person you were born to be. Believe in yourself. Speak well of yourself and others, and use the power of your imagination to send positive love to heal your own hurts and the wounds of the world."

"How can I do all of this?"

"Practice thinking with your Heart"

And

"Speaking from your Soul"

"Yes, but aren't there times in life when you are scared, or tired, when your energy or faith seems low? When you lose confidence in yourself, and forget to care for others?"

"Yes, and there are things you can do to rebuild your energy and faith. Some people Pray"

And

"Others Meditate"

"Some people do both. They are very similar, but words can be very important in life. Sometimes people feel better calling the same thing by a different name."

"Sometimes, you will also just need to rest and do nothing at all. Just be still and wait for the world to catch up with you, or for trouble to pass, or for the list of choices available to shorten as you try to weigh them up."

Fionn could hear Bovmall speak, "There are two very important Prayers or Meditations - whichever you choose to call them - which will help you through the day and the night. One is the Morning Prayer for guidance through the day. There are dangers in the world and always temptation to do the wrong thing, to make the wrong choice, to treat others unkindly, or to lose faith in yourself. But nobody ever travels through life alone. We are in the company of Love and Positive Energy. Our Guardian Angel travels with us to protect us."

And Lia Luchra was there too, "We can take time each morning to remember the presence of this guide as a way to gather ourselves and our energy and emotional courage before we face the world; to ask for help through the day."

Guardian Angel Prayer

Angel of God, my Guardian dear
To whom God's love commits me here.
Ever this day be at my side
To light and guard, to rule and guide.
Amen.

Fionn wondered, "I'm not sure about Guardian Angels? How can we know they exist when we never see them?"

"Ah, Faith a Stór." Bovmall's usual answer when Fionn doubted something in life.

"Your Guardian Angel is always with you, even when times seem most tricky. Have you ever left home in the morning and then remembered you forgot something, and had to go back home to collect it, and then been late by a few minutes? Well, that is just one example of your Guardian Angel protecting you from some danger that you can not see or predict, but that you were saved from by being a few minutes late going out into the world that morning.

Lia Luachra seemed more definite, "There are also times in life when you can see your Guardian Angel. Angels can take the shape of many different things or people, especially at times when you need them most."

"Your Guardian Angel might appear as a beautiful butterfly that, if you follow, will lead you to something quite magical. Or a stranger you meet who has a pearl of wisdom to give to you, if only you had eyes to see and ears to hear."

"What is the second Prayer or Meditation?" Fionn wondered.

"It is the Prayer or Meditation before you sleep at the end of the day. In your morning reflections, you ask your God for the gift of emotional courage to face the challenges and choices you will face in the day."

"In your evening prayer, you ask for grace to accept all that has been given to you during the day. Sometimes, this involves giving thanks for precious gifts; sometimes, it involves asking for strength to accept a great challenge."

"But always know, you will never have to face a challenge in life that you will be unable to achieve. The world does not work like that. Your life is a journey. You are always growing, developing - becoming your true self; realising the truth of who you were born to be."

Fionn stirred himself from the half sleep by the fireside and headed off to his bed. Just before he went to sleep, he took time to remember his day, finding his breath, giving thanks, asking for peace and praying to the God he believed in.

Prayer Before Sleep

Now I lay me down to sleep

I pray to God my Soul to keep

Four corners on my bed

Four Angels overhead

Guide me safely through this night

And wake me with the mornings light

Amen

After his evening prayer, he found his sleep was more restful, his dreams less frightening. And when he woke in the morning, he found it easier to make meaning from the messages he heard in his dreams.

Being Visited in His Dreams by His Mother

~e2~

O ne night, at the age of six, when Fionn was sleeping, his mother visited him, in a dream. Some would say that Fionn slept like all six-year-olds do, with one eye open and an ear afraid to close! Some say, only children who are afraid or searching for something sleep like this. But with one eye open and an ear to hear Fionn saw his mother, and knew her face. He listened as she sang to him and told him stories of his father and, just before he awoke, she whispered his destiny into his ear. When he woke his mother had gone.

Fionn's Aunts told him stories of his father too - of his courage and strength, and how he had been the chief of the Fianna of Ireland. His aunts told Fionn stories of how he too was born to be brilliant and strong and fast and brave. Fionn liked to listen to these tales but he also felt afraid and unsure in the face of his future and the world of unknowns outside of his childhood home.

Fionn often tried very hard to remember what his mother had whispered to him about his destiny in his dream that night. But each time he tried, he seemed to remember her words differently. Sometimes he began to doubt that she had ever really visited him at all. Sometimes he wondered if he had only imagined the dream he had remembered that night. But always somewhere deep down inside, he felt he remembered her saying something to him about meeting the Wise One, and fishing for beautiful poems and magical wisdom by a beautiful lake in the heart of Ireland.

Fionn often wished and prayed that he could hear his mother's voice even just once more so he could remember to ask her who he was born to be.

Fionn grew older and stronger in the care of his Aunts. And, as he did, they worried more and more about him. They forbid that he climb trees, and warned him about the stings of nettles. But every six-year-old knows that nettle stings wear off, and that even the highest tree is no fun once it has been climbed twice. Each day he would travel deeper and deeper into the woods. He would spend more and more time away from home each day and, as time passed his Aunts even stopped calling him home for his tea, trusting that he would turn up when he got hungry.

One day Fionn did come home and, just from looking at him, his Aunts knew that something had happened to him in the woods which had changed him forever. Some might say that Fionn had just reached that age of boyhood where it was time for him to leave home. Others might say it was just the next step in his own personal journey in the search for who he was born to be. But, whatever the truth, something had changed. Something that meant Fionn would have to leave his Aunts and their care before very long.

BEALTAINE
The Courage to follow Your Path

~e2~

F ionn woke to face the beginning of the rest of his life. He began the day with a prayer to his Guardian Angel. He thought of how his Aunts had taught him that the best way of praying is to sit still and listen very carefully to the voice of wisdom within, and to ask the God you believe in for the gift needed to help you through the day.

Fionn prayed for the gift of courage to face the adventure of moving into the next phase of his life. He felt how his heart began to pound and a fiery energy stir throughout his body. And as he listened carefully to his inner God, he heard the words of wisdom:

"Believe in yourself. Believe in yourself."

Legend says that Fionn left the home and care of his Aunts to join a gang of young wild teenage boys who were roaming throughout the land of Ireland at the time. Some say that his Aunts' fears of raising Fionn as a teenager caused them to reject him; offering Fionn - maybe even before he was ready - to the world. Others say that such a time comes for every boy-child who feels the call to travel and explore the world in the company of other young men.

But as legend had it, Fionn left the only home he had ever known to run away with a gang of young men who travelled the land playing games and having sport, drinking and dancing and fighting as all such groups of young men left alone are wont to do.

Some might wonder at how sad Fionn might have been at having to leave the only home he had ever known - now left to face the world alone, to make his own way in life, the strange shock of it all, the sudden change in his comfort and circumstance.

Others might be surprised at how quickly and easily Fionn seemed to take to his new adventure. Maybe because he still heard the voice of his mother who had visited him in a dream and spoke to him the secret of his destiny. Fionn knew he was starting out on the path of his own self-discovery. The journey that is life itself: in search of his Soul's Path.

The other part of this story is that it was now early summer and many young people leave their home for the first time in summertime. Something about the fullness of life: the awakening of the world and growing up.

Fionn loved summer, or, more precisely, Fionn enjoyed each new season when its time had come. He was not afraid of change as some people are. By the time summer arrived, Fionn had grown tired of spring; he was always eager for the promise of a new beginning. Each season brought with it the promise of new gifts. Fionn had grown up close to Nature and he never forgot the lesson that everything has its place in the rhythm of the world. This thought helped him, especially when he could not fully understand why certain things happened the way they did in life. He remembered the wisdom of his Aunts when he would ask them to explain such mysteries:

"There is always a reason, Fionn. Even when you do not understand, you must trust that God who sees all has his reason - that is what they mean when they say, 'Thy will be done'."

"It is often only when time passes, and you can look back on a part of your life, that you can begin to make some sense of all that happened. It is only afterwards that you can begin to tell a story about all that has happened in your life."

Just as Fionn accepted change, and even looked forward to new beginnings, neither was he afraid of letting go of things, of endings. He knew that summer could never be unless spring had ended. Or, that if days lasted forever, there would be no nights or time to rest.

Bovmall used to say that, "We need endings in life so that new life can begin; that is life."

Lia Luachra used to warn that, "Many people live their lives trying always to avoid endings, saying goodbye, or moving on. They fear the pain of loss. But loss is inevitable, if you choose to live your life to the fullest possibility you have been given. Emotional Warriors know that to live fully - to experience all the joy in the world - means that you will, at times, also have to experience loss and pain."

Bovmall then spoke quietly, "Death is a type of loss. Death is also the only certainty in life, yet it is the one thing most people are too afraid to even talk about. But if we faced up to our fear of death, we could then begin to enjoy living life. People fight and argue and worry about all sorts of things that are simply not important, just to help to trick themselves into thinking they are really alive and that they will be able to avoid death forever. But death waits for nobody."

Lia Luchra often began her day standing barefoot in the garden with her arms outstretched to the sky saying to anyone who would listen, "Today is a good day to die!"

When Fionn asked her what she meant she explained:

"I like to remind myself that I might die today, and that reminds me that if today was my last day to live, I had better choose to live it as best as I can – and so – today's a good day to die – because it's a great day to live."

Loss, Death, and the Wake of Life

~ez~

In Ireland there is a saying, 'the dead are not gone far away.' People keep this saying because they believe it - they know it to be true. When someone dies in Ireland, there is a very special funeral ritual that takes place called the 'Wake.' It was called a Wake because everybody stayed awake all through the night to watch over the body of the person - telling stories, drinking and crying.

In olden days, the 'Wake' happened in the person's home and all sorts of people would gather to pay their respects: relatives and friends, as well those who had disagreed or competed with the person in their life. These Wakes could last for days. A sacred time given over to honouring both the sadness and pain of losing someone from this world, but also a celebration and thanks for their time in this life. People stayed with the body while the Soul journeyed to the spirit world.

Seanachaís and storytellers attended the Wake telling all sorts of stories about the person's life, so that all sides of the person could be remembered and celebrated. There was also a very special person in attendance at the wake: the Bean Caoineadh - the keening woman! The Bean Caoineadh's job was to lead the company in crying. These women were professional criers, and they could get even the hardest heart to shed a tear for the person before them.

Fionn's Aunts had taught him that this expression of deep grief - the crying, lamenting and 'Waking' of the person - was seen as a very sacred ritual, for two very special reasons.

Bovmall warned that, "The pain of tears and sadness of deep grief is very dangerous if someone tries to keep it hidden inside of them. It is impossible to keep such pain within your body, and if you do not cry it out it will find its own way out. Such pain, when kept hidden, can cause even the strongest man to die from a broken heart."

Lia Luachra added that, "The other reason for the Wake, the storytelling, and the crying, is to call the Spirits and Souls from the other world to meet and bring the dead person's Soul safely to the other side. Some people call the other world 'Heaven.' They do not realise how close we are to Heaven; how the Souls of those who go before us are always around us, protecting us, guiding us, giving us advice and wisdom.

Fionn knew this to be true. From a very young age, he knew that when he was scared, or frightened, or unsure, all he had to do was close his eyes and pray to his father. Even though Fionn had never met his father in this world, he felt he knew him. He could see him when he closed his eyes. He could feel his protection when he needed him most.

Absent Parents

~e2~

K nowing that his father had died, and believing that even in death our Souls live on in a Heaven, that is much closer to us than many imagine, brought a comfort and ease to Fionn.

However, missing his absent mother brought a very different sense of loss and confusion for Fionn. He knew she was not dead, and yet she was not with him. He had heard different stories of why she had abandoned him as a child. Some said - that she loved him so much she gave him up because she knew she would not be able to care and protect him. Others had said that she must give her child up for his own protection and safety. Even more said that she had given him up because she had fallen in love with another man after Fionn's father, Uail, had been killed.

The absence of a truthful story for Fionn was like an ache that would not go away. It ate into his very heart and crept up on him, often at the most unexpected times. Not just on his Birthday or Christmas, but other times too - times when people might never expect or even know.

Fionn knew that death was one type of ending, but separation was something quite different. It felt like emptiness inside of him, something he could never quite put his finger on or explain. He remembered how, as a child, his Aunts had tried to comfort him when he felt this sort of loneliness.

Bovmall used to say: "Sometimes it's like as if you walked into a field and there is sadness all around you, sadness in the air and on the land – but the sadness is not of your making."

At the times she'd say this Fionn was never quite sure what she meant by it. But, since then, he had often remembered her words and at times he felt how much sense she made. Lia Luchra would join in too, "there is a hole at the Heart of everyone" she'd say "a hole that only a story can fill."

Fionn always wondered if the feeling of a hole in his Heart, the emptiness he felt he carried around inside of himself, could only be filled by the story of who he was born to be.

Most often the ache of not knowing who he was born to be crept up on him in the late evening; when his day's work was done and he was tired. When the dusk light changed, Fionn found himself staring off into the distance, wondering what was the truth of his being?

Running with the youngsters brought a welcome relief for Fionn. He found himself too busy most of the time to spend time thinking about the difficult questions of life. He went on for a very long time pretending to himself that such questions did not really matter.

Fionn was growing older now. Travelling through this time in his life, surrounded by the fun and excitement of this gang of new-found friends, Fionn spent less and less time in prayer or meditation. It seemed to him that so few others now believed in prayer, he began to doubt himself. He also found it harder to pray in the company of others who did not seem to believe in prayers or to practice meditation. And, anyway, the gang of friends always seemed too busy to take time out of a busy life for sane moments of quiet reflection or relaxation.

Except, Fionn never quite gave up on his faith in prayer and meditation and, from time to time, he found himself falling back into the old habits of sitting quietly by himself and turning to God for help or advice. Sometimes Fionn also remembered to talk with God, just to say thanks.

Fionn loved the quiet times when he found himself alone, at peace, unrushed or troubled by the world. Times when he walked in nature and remembered the beauty of the world. Fionn loved even the rain.

Summer Showers and Rainbows

~e2~

S ummer showers were different to winter showers. Summer showers came upon the world more quickly - they seemed to have a secret reason, but they did not have the type of rain that was as wet or cold as winter rain. Fionn believed summer rain was sent to wash away the sadness or darkness of the last of the winter greyness.

Fionn never feared being caught in the rain. He used to laugh at the sight of others running, here and there, trying to avoid the raindrops. They got just as wet, and yet they seemed to waste their energy in trying to go against God's will.

Fionn enjoyed the rain, and, when he did get caught out in a shower, he thought of it as God's holy water washing away some trouble or pain. When he opened his heart to think like this, Fionn found the water warmer, softer, and renewing.

The other beauty of summer showers was the rainbows that God sent after the rain - rainbows watching over the world, the healing beauty of colour, and light, and God's warmth for all people.

Fionn was always amazed by people's reactions to rainbows. The saddest part is just how many people simply do not even notice the beauty of a rainbow - too busy rushing here or there to remember to look into the sky above. The other reaction for many is to rush off in excitement to find the end of the rainbow - one old Irish legend tells of a hidden Crock of Gold to be found at the end of the rainbow. Another legend sings a song about somewhere over the rainbow.

Fionn pitied those who spent their lives in the constant pursuit of false promises, waiting for a tomorrow that might never come. Fionn knew that the real beauty and gift of the rainbow was not to be looked for somewhere over the rainbow, or at the end of the rainbow, but was here, now, under the rainbow.

Fionn sat down, feeling the strength of the earth beneath his body, always constant; the earth came to meet his every step. He looked to the wonder of the sky above and counted the colours of the rainbow: Red, Orange, Yellow, Green, Blue, Indigo, and Violet. Seven layers, connected, yet different. Someone once wondered if the seven colours of the rainbow were like the seven chakras – the special centres of energy in each and every human being? Or if they were a colour for every day of the week?

Fionn knew that the others in his gang of friends were gone off, rushing here and there to find the crock of gold. He felt glad of the quiet time to himself, yet, he felt a sadness for his friends who were still making one of the greatest mistakes a person can make in life. That is the mistake of following another person's dream. They had not yet learned that every single person in this world can find their own treasure but, to do so, means following your own path: the path that is true to your own dream.

Fionn closed his eyes, keeping the image of the rainbow in his mind's eye. He breathed each one of the seven colours of the rainbow into his body, taking time to feel the beauty, and warmth and spiritual energy of each colour fill his entire body - reaching through him from the tips of his toes right through to the top of his head.

He remembered the beauty of prayer and meditation, and the healing, relaxing power of breathing deep into his belly the energy and life giving breath of God's world.

Slowly, when the time felt right for Fionn, he opened his eyes again. The world looked brighter, and more beautiful than he had remembered. Fionn thought to himself how every time we open our eyes, the world we see before us is the world we have made for ourselves: wherever we are, whatever we see before us, is our world. If only we took time to notice the things we have collected and kept close - the things that made up our life - the people, the possessions, the choices, that we have gathered around us.

Fionn realised that our world is a creation of how we choose it to be. It is as simple as opening our eyes and looking at all that we have in our life. This idea also made him realise that, if we do not love what we see when we open our eyes, then what we need to do is stand up and make a choice to create a new world for ourselves. Fionn knew that this was the journey of all Emotional Warriors, including himself.

Fionn noticed that the rainbow had disappeared again, and he thought to himself just how important it is in life to take God's gifts when they are offered to us. Moments pass and with them opportunities. There is a cusp to every wave and, if we do not take our chance in life, we might miss it.

Fionn stood up and began to walk again. He could hear the gang of friends approaching; annoyed with themselves that they had yet again been unable to find their treasure.

The Danger of Youth

~e2~

L egend had it that Fionn and this gang of friends and youngsters were known throughout the countryside. Their voice was such that they could be heard long before they would ever arrive. Their antics were such that they were spoken of long after they had left a place. Many had cause to complain about how they behaved, giving out about their wild and reckless misbehaviour. Others said of them that they were no different to any other gang of teenage boys who were left alone too long unsupervised by a caring adult or a wise mentor.

Bovmall used to say: "youth is wasted on the young."

Then Lia Luachra would reply saying: "wisdom's wasted on the old."

Fionn used to think to himself, at times like this, that they were now more conscious of growing old. The sadness of age, Fionn thought, was how often older people either forgot the pleasure in the fiery playfulness of youth, or how often they remembered they had never taken the chance to experience real passion in their own lives.

Yet, there is a real danger in groups of teenagers left to their own company without the guidance and advice of a good mentor. The dangers of such groups were well warned about in many stories. In their wisdom Fionn's Aunts knew that, left alone, this group of teenagers would indeed bring trouble on themselves.

Fionn's Aunts heard all about his escapades with this gang, no matter how far away he thought he was. Some believed that his Aunts, having known Fionn so well as a young child, actually knew what he would do ever before he did it himself. His Aunts feared that the noise and antics of this group would surely attract the attention of the clan-Morna – who would realise that Fionn was amongst the group and come after him as legend had threatened.

Indeed, it wasn't long before the group of friends did run into real danger that brought a sudden and shocking end to their carefree recklessness. Some thought it was the clan-Morna who came upon the band of merry makers, when a travelling rogue confronted them and killed each and every one of them in the fiercest slaughter ever seen in the land. Yet, when it came to Fionn's turn to be slain, it was not his strength that saved him - although he was tall and broad and strong. Nor was it his speed - for he could now run faster than even the deer in the forest, but he did not run away.

Fionn did not fear death itself, but Fionn felt terrified and alone: the terror of the violence, the senselessness of it all, the waste of good life. He prayed for guidance. His fear made it harder for him to listen, but in the moment's silence before his death he heard his Aunts' wisdom: 'when you meet resistance, turn away.' Fionn sat down in the face of the Temper Monster who was about to slay him. Expecting Fionn to put up a fight like the others, the Temper Monster was caught completely off-guard by Fionn's passive reaction. The monster didn't know what to do - it was as if the energy in the moment had suddenly changed.

Fionn was still trembling; although finding himself grounded, supported more fully by the solid presence of the earth, brought a greater sense of comfort and safety. He remembered the calming strength of belly breathing and he counted his breaths deep into his belly: one, two, three. Then breathing out: one, two, three.

His Aunts had always advised him when he felt frightened or scared, to breathe in God's love deeply into his centre within. Fionn felt a little bit better, although he slowly began to worry that the Temper Monster would soon begin to terrorise him again. Then he heard a voice speak from his centre within:

"Always believe in yourself. Always believe in yourself."

Fionn stood up. He felt more solid and safe having breathed God's love deep into his centre. Fionn found his voice, and spoke with an honest confidence that only comes when you speak from the heart:

"I am Fionn, son of Uail, true Chieftain of the Fianna of Ireland."

With these words, the Temper Monster became a broken man and fell to his knees. In this moment, Fionn saw a side to this man that nobody else had seen in a very long time indeed. This man had hidden his own fear and vulnerability behind his anger and rage. He cried for seven days and Fionn stayed with him to care for him.

Fionn realised that just as there are two sides to every story, there are at least two sides to every person. In fact, Fionn knew that, all we are as human beings are the stories we tell about ourselves.

We are born into stories. We live our lives creating stories, in search of a true story of ourselves; telling stories about ourselves, changing stories, retelling stories.

We are story-telling beings.

Sharing the Story of Who We Are

~ez~

A ll we actually have in life is the story we can tell about ourselves. When we meet and greet people, we introduce ourselves through the stories we share. Fionn and the Temper Monster met in this moment with the traditional Irish greeting.

"Dia duit, an bhfuil aon scéal agat?"

(God's blessing, tell us the story about yourself.)

"Diabhal scéal, muna bhfuil aon scéal agat féin."

(Devil a story, if you will not share a story about yourself too.)

It was in this moment, when the two were willing to join in the sharing of stories, that they began to find their friendship, and intimacy. Since real friendship requires both people to share, real intimacy develops only when both people are prepared to give and take, and to work hard. Being two solitary souls - one a man (and men love to teach), the other a boy (and boys love to learn) - it is said that these two had much in common and enjoyed their time together, sharing their stories. You might be surprised just how much Fionn and the Temper Monster had in common.

Legend has it that the Temper Monster was indeed Fionn's uncle, a brother of Uail's. And when Uail was killed by the clan-Morna, his brother had run away in fear and rage, hiding himself in the deepest part of the forest, turning his anger out, killing any and all who passed his way. It was not until he had been confronted with the name of his pain, that he could face his hurt.

During their time together, the Temper Monster spoke with Fionn about three things: absent parents, concealed anger, and healing relationships. And Fionn had reached a time in his life where he was able to listen.

"When your father was killed by the clan-Morna, I could not face my grief and fear. I was afraid I might die too; I was afraid that if I allowed myself to grieve, I would fall apart. I also felt guilty that my brother had died and I had not been able to save him. I believed that if I kept my pain and feelings of sadness and guilt to myself, hidden inside, they would go away. But they never did go away – they seemed to grow bigger – and, the bigger they seemed to grow inside, the angrier I became. And I was hurting more too, except I would not let anyone see or know my pain. To stop people getting close to me and my pain, I began to hit out and snap at those who were closest to me. Those who loved me most suffered most. When I had succeeded in turning away all those who tried to love and care for me, I tried to lose myself: I had begun to hate myself so it didn't matter to me that nobody else would like me. I went away, trying to lose myself in the deepest part of the forest. I didn't want anyone to come near me and when they did, like you and your friends, I fought them off. I turned all my inner anger and rage out against the world. My heart had grown so cold, nothing could live anywhere near me. I killed the beauty and life in everything."

Fionn was not afraid to ask questions of the Temper Monster, "What were you searching for in the darkest part of the forest?"

"I think I was looking for the memory, or the voice, of your father. I have heard people talk about a 'father wound,' when people are left by a father who chooses not to live with them, or who dies, or even a father who does not have it within his ability to give the care and love to his children. When this happens, children are left limping through life wounded emotionally, searching in vain hope for that which their father could never give them, but which he was never able to admit to either. Do you know what I mean?"

"I think so," thought Fionn. "But it is my mother I miss. She left me, and I do not know why or where she has gone. It feels like a 'mother wound.' I think I see her sometimes in daydreams and nightmares. At night, I feel an emptiness, an ache, a wonder of who I was born to be"

"I think you are right: a mother can let us down or hurt us just as much as a father might. It's different for different people, but everybody hurts sometimes. We are left to try to find those answers for ourselves. That is what the journey is all about. The journey between two points in time - from the person you were born to be to the person you have become. Absent parents, or parents who do not tell us the full truth about ourselves, really add to the difficulties of that journey in life. We are given many more questions which other children simply do not ever have to face."

"How do we ever manage then to make it through the journey of this life, without ending up lost in the darkest part of the forest? Without turning all our pain and upset into anger and rage, keeping everyone who would care for us from ever getting close to our true selves?"

"We manage, Fionn, thanks to the people we meet along the way. Every single person we meet has a special message for us, some people carry very special gifts for us. Those people offer us what I call the 'gift of healing relationships.' They are the people sent by God to teach us how to trust, and share, and love all over again. It is never, ever too late to learn these things, Fionn. For some people learning how to trust or love takes a very long time, usually because we have not yet met the right person to teach us."

The Gift of Healing Relationships

"The beauty of God's love is that each and every one of us is able to experience real love. We are loving and loveable beings. You must remember, Fionn, no matter how painful or sad your past has been, the fact that you are here right now proves that you have overcome these troubles. All of us, Fionn, are more than our pasts. We are the living embodiment of our life's potential. We are what we dream we will become."

It may seem strange to some that even the Temper Monster had something of value to gift to Fionn. But in the time spent sharing and caring for each other, Fionn experienced the healing power of relationships and came to understand some more parts of who he was born to be. The fact that Fionn was learning this wisdom from the Temper Monster, in the deepest part of the forest, was something that his Aunts, however, did not quite understand.

Legend says at this point in the story, and at this time in his life, Fionn's Aunts came to find him and they took him back to live with them. Some say it was out of their true fear for his safety that they came looking for him - afraid of the dangers he might face in the world outside the safety of their home. Others say it was as a consequence of their own jealousy, watching him being cared for by another. But either way, it was not very long before Fionn's Aunts came for him and brought him back to live with them again.

LUGHNASA
The Echo of Who You Were Born to Be

~e2~

Fionn returned to live with his Aunts, but enough had changed in Fionn's life for nothing to be the same as it once was before. Fionn was older now, as were his Aunts. He cared more for them than they could for him. More than this, however, Fionn knew in his heart that he had tasted the beginning of the journey of who he was to be. In the wisdom that only comes with age, Fionn's Aunts also knew that he had also tasted enough of the world to make it impossible for him to go back to being the little boy they used to know.

It was not a decision they made in their heads, but a feeling they shared in their hearts. All three of them knew that the time would soon come again for Fionn to leave the place he had known as home, in search of the story of who he really was.

Autumn Sadness

~e2~

Fionn knew his mood had changed, and it was more than the autumn. He was sure it had something to do with his searching for the story of who he was born to be. He left the place he had come to call home for the second time. This time he knew that, somewhere within himself, he was carrying a sadness that would not go away. As he journeyed, he became more and more aware of the growing sense of loss. Fionn felt as if the empty hole inside his Heart was growing bigger in some strange way. When he thought about how he felt, it reminded him of walking into the field of sadness his Aunt had spoken of before – this time though it felt to Fionn as if his Soul was getting ready to walk into a field of sadness he had not yet met. It felt, to Fionn, as though his sense of sadness was almost in anticipation for a loss that was yet to come into his life.

For some people, this type of feeling emotions about things before they ever happened might seem strange, but, having grown up close to nature, Fionn could read the signs that forewarned a pending loss. Autumn time always warned a loss of life, a natural rhythm of change. The leaves of summer green changed, and soon fell away laying bare the hidden secrets of the true shape of the trees beneath. Fionn was always surprised at how different the world looked when the camouflage of foliage fell away.

He wondered about how much of what we see in life is a type of camouflage, a façade we hide behind, like a mask that people put on to hide their true inner selves and real emotions. Fionn wondered about how often we simply say we're grand or fine and hide behind a smile when people ask us how we are.

Fionn remembered his Aunts' wise words when Bovmall used to say, "The world would be a kinder place if we took time to mind each other's broken hearts."

And Lia Luachra used to smile and say, "Ara-sure heartbreak makes the heart grow kinder."

Fionn wondered how different the world would look if we could see the sadness each other carries hidden in our hearts as we go about the day and night. He could read the other signs too: the swallows and their summer young gathered in the early days of autumn, they too knew it was time to leave, to take flight for something new.

Nature knows that nothing stays the same. Loss is part of life and the cycle of change brings new beginnings.

Fionn remembered how, sometimes as a child, he used to worry about his emotions and moods. Sometimes he felt tired, sometimes he felt sad, sometimes he felt hungry, or happy, or excited, or scared, or ashamed. Sometimes his moods and emotions changed very quickly, and sometimes it felt confusing as if two or more feelings were getting all mixed up together and Fionn could not be clear about what exactly he was feeling or why.

Sometimes when his moods changed suddenly, Fionn knew that there was often a good reason. For example, sometimes when he felt tired, he knew he had to rest. Often it was because he had tired himself out with play or hard work. His Aunts were always good at reminding him to rest one day a week, to give thanks for all he had done, and also to gather his strength and emotional courage for the week that was to follow.

Fionn remembered talking with his Aunts once about the strangeness of people's moods and how they can sometimes change quite unexpectedly.

Bovmall spoke first as she often did: "Many people become frightened of their own moods and try to just have one type of mood all of the time, like happiness, or friendliness. But why do people fear or reject what is just another part of themselves?"

Lia Luachra continued: "Even if our mood is angry or sad, that mood is part of us and we should not try to get rid of that part of ourselves. We need all parts of our being, even bad moods are necessary; they can help and protect us at very important times in our lives."

Fionn found that, when he could remember to accept all of his moods, life was much easier for him and those around him too. There were even times when he felt like just staying in bed all day long and not having to face the world at all. He found the best way to deal with moods was to feed them, to go with them, to allow them into his life. So on days like that he simply stayed in bed. They were wonderful days too.

Something else his Aunts had said about moods - something that Fionn had not quite fully understood but liked the sound of anyway - was that: "Moods are often influenced by something outside of our control. Something much bigger than we are: Our Stars, and the Moon, and the Heavens, and the Gods - all have an influence on how we are, how we feel, our energy, and our destiny."

His Aunts had said quite a bit more about the Heavens and the Stars, but all that had made sense to Fionn was the bit about how hard many people find it is to sleep on nights when there is a full moon. Fionn listened to this because he could never sleep on nights when there was a full moon, but it never worried him since, on these nights, he never felt he needed to sleep; he seemed to be filled with a new kind of energy.

Time and Travel

~e2~

Fionn travelled through the length and breadth of Ireland in search of the story of who he was born to be. His journey brought him from the four most extreme parts of the compass, from the North to the South, from the East to the West. He journeyed and searched.

Fionn enjoyed travelling; he was always excited by the chance to visit somewhere new in the world, and to take the chance of meeting new people and learning the stories of their ways of living. He enjoyed hearing other people's stories more than he enjoyed telling them about himself. Sometimes he wondered if this was because he was never really sure of how his own story began, and why, after his father had died, his own mother really gave him over to the care of his two Aunts. Fionn wondered if he knew the truth of this part of his story, would he find more strength in his own voice in the company of others.

Fionn enjoyed travelling, as it was one sure way of meeting new and exciting people. But even more than meeting people with different ways of living and different stories to tell, Fionn loved to travel because of how it seemed to do strange things to both light and time.

Fionn always felt that when he was on a journey, he saw God's light in a new way. Maybe it was because he was awake earlier in the mornings and later into the evening time, but he always seemed to notice the beauty of the sunrise and sunsets when he journeyed. It was almost as if his eyes were able to open even wider, taking in more of the light, and wonder and beauty of God's creations. It was as if, sometimes, Fionn was so aware and open to the world, that he felt he would never need to rest again – he was almost afraid to sleep in case he would miss seeing something new and magical.

It was at times like this when Fionn remembered to see the simple things in life, that he realised how the world is full of magic - if only we had eyes to see and ears to hear: the beauty of a sunrise or sunset, the magic meaning hidden in the first birdsong of the day, or how to wait for night to fall and wish upon a falling star.

In magic moments like this it seemed to Fionn that time itself changed shape and speed. In a strange way, it seemed to Fionn as though, sometimes, often at exactly the same moment, time seemed to race faster than ever before, while also standing still, so that anything in the whole world was possible to achieve – right there and then.

Fionn was always amazed about how people spoke about time. Some people never seemed to have enough time; they talked about running out of time and wishing they could make more time to do something they had previously put off doing. Other people spoke about taking time or stealing time - always dreaming of what they might do tomorrow, rather than enjoying what they had right now. These people never found the secret of living in the moment. So many people in the world missed the moment since they were too busy doing things. They had become - Fionn thought to himself - human doings, rather than human beings.

Even for Fionn, though, these magic moments, while all around, were more often missed rather than witnessed. Fionn thought to himself: "You really need to feel comfortable with yourself, to be able to live in the moment, to be able to BE." But he also knew deep down that since he had begun to feel the ache of who he was born to be - since he began to hear the echo of his past - since he began to search for the story of who he was born to be - he had not felt comfortable enough to be in the moment. He was on a journey, which held the promise of the truth of who he was born to be but, in all his searching and doing, the very truth he yearned for seemed to constantly evade him.

Losing Hope and Energy

Legend spoke of how Fionn would travel throughout the lands of Ireland in the search of who he was born to be. He longed for answers to the questions in his Heart. Who he was, what was his father really like and was he really anything like him? What was the truth in the story of why his mother had given him over to the care of his Aunts? And, what was the truth of his destiny? And so, Fionn travelled the lands from North to South, and East to West, trying to discover the truth of who he was born to be

Over time Fionn could feel his hope and energy leaving his body. It was as though the search in vain drained him of his very belief in himself. Throughout his journey in the search of who he was, Fionn encountered many rejections and hurts in the search for the answers he dreamed for. He seemed to search in vain sometimes for someone who could give him some answers, or make sense to him of where he came from and where he was going in life and what he was meant to do.

His search for who he was born to be seemed like it had somehow become a real struggle now, filled with loss and pain of rejections and lost hope. Fionn's mood changed and he felt sure the change in mood was more than just the change to autumn season. He was sure it had something to do with his searching for the story of who he really was. It now felt to Fionn as if his serach for who he was to be had become too much for him. He felt like giving up.

Fionn felt as if he could hear an echo - of who he was born to be – singing inside his head somewhere. But the echo had now become like a constant deafening drumbeat that he could not loosen from within his head. The ache he felt for the truth of his story had grown to become an intolerable pain that he felt would only end by the breaking of his heart. He felt like letting go.

Fionn began to lose sight of where he wanted to go, and lose faith in his own ability to even take one more step. He had never felt like this before, and the fear of his own failure was something he could not ease. He thought he must be reaching the end of his strength, the end of his courage, the end of his wisdom. He wondered whether this was what some people called a crisis or a break down.

As Fionn tried to keep himself together, to keep going with the very last of what he had to give, he heard the distant voices of both the Temper Monster and his Aunts.

"When you are tired, rest."

"Be careful never to try to keep your pain inside of yourself - hidden pain will kill you."

"Remember the healing power of tears."

Fionn was not sure if he actually made a choice, but he began to cry uncontrollably. He fell to the ground exhausted. At that moment, he lost all sense of time and place. He had no idea either how long he had been crying, or where in the world he really was.

Through his crying, Fionn began to hear the sound of music he had never heard before, soothing and soft, yet challenging and definite. It beat in rhythm of his tears, and the drumming of his Heart. The music seemed to come from a place at the very centre within.

As he tried to listen to the tune the music turned into a voice that Fionn had never heard before; it was not the voice of any of those he had met on his journey. It was something else. The voice seemed to draw closer until it was as if the voice stood just beside Fionn, or just before him, or behind him. It was as if the voice came from within Fionn.

"Look up, Fionn. Open your eyes and look out. The world seen through eyes with tears is a very special world indeed."

Fionn looked up and was amazed by the simple beauty of the world he saw. It was as if his tears had cleaned the colours of the world - as if his tears had made his eyes fit to look upon the world anew. His tears made him able to see the possibilities of life in a new way.

The Fifth Province- The Centre Within

~ez~

As he opened his eyes wider, the voice seemed to become clearer, and the music continued to play most beautifully. Fionn looked about and, close by, saw the image of what seemed to be a very old woman dressed in a black shawl; some might have called her a tramp or a traveller. Her hair looked untidy, her clothes dirty. Fionn thought she might even be a foreigner due to the darkness of her skin.

Fionn spoke to her, "Where am I?"

She spoke softly, "You are at the Centre Within, and you have reached Ireland's Fifth Province."

"What's the Fifth Province?" Fionn wondered.

The Tramp spoke with both a sense of confidence and magic, "The Fifth Province is the centre within Ireland. Your journey brought you to the four provinces of Ireland - Ulster, Munster, Leinster and Connacht - in search of your story. But Fionn, - stories come from five places: the North, where you can often find trouble; the South, where you can sometimes find a friend; the East, where all stories begin; and the West, where all stories that begin also end; and, the fifth place, the Centre Within."

"In Irish legend, there was a Fifth Province - maybe real, maybe imaginary - what is the difference? It is a place at the very heart of Ireland, at the mythical Hill of Uisneach, where the High King or Queen of Ireland sat and heard disputes, and conversations, and storytelling from the other four provinces of Ireland. The only place where there remains evidence of the trace of the Fifth Province is in the Irish language itself, where the word is the same for fifth and province. An 'Cúige–Cúige,' a very special and sacred place indeed. It is the place where people go when they need to re-imagine their lives or to find a new way of looking at old problems in their lives, and communities. Do you understand?"

"No," replied Fionn. "Is the Fifth Province somewhere people go to decide who is in the right or wrong? Where someone or other is judged to be the winner of the argument?"

"No," the Tramp shook her head. "The Fifth Province is a very special place, Fionn, where everyone can be a winner. There are no losers; and there is no need for competition. They pick their words very carefully in the Fifth Province; they speak in the tongues of poets. All sides of the story hold some parts of the truth; nobody has a monopoly on the truth, and nobody is exempt from making a mistake."

"So how did I get here?" wondered Fionn.

"You have been searching for a story that will tell you the truth of who you were born to be. You have put so much energy and time into a journey throughout this world. Many people make the same mistake, Fionn; they travel the world when they are trying to find themselves! When the quickest way to find yourself is to rest very patiently and quietly, just with yourself. The journey of self-discovery, Fionn, is a journey inwards, to your Centre Within. It is not an outward journey, yet people are afraid to venture into their core being. They are afraid of what they might find."

"Yes, but if this centre within is both such a magical and feared place, how did I make it here?"

"Well, you found the Fifth Province when you journeyed to the edge of the four other provinces. You had to go to the edge to find your centre. It's the same with finding your Centre Within Fionn - you fell into it - you could not avoid it. In fact, the only way to find your centre is to fall into it. There is no map that can show you the way into your interior."

"I still do not understand?"

"Well, Fionn, it's like this. So many people try to avoid the fall. They are terrified of it, and they call it all sorts of things: a break down, a break up, a crisis, a death, a conversion. But each of us has a fall - we have to have it - it is the fall in life that brings us back to our Soul's Path. It reminds us that our destiny in life has been set out for us before we were even born. We cannot deny the destiny of who we were born to be."

The Tramp seemed to think to herself for a moment and then continued; "As we grow in life, we create a world for ourselves, full of different types of things that we think are important to who we are: jobs, money, all sorts of friends to tell us all sorts of things - false Gods, if you want to call them that. But it's not until we have our fall, that we see the really important things we have been given in life: things like love and friendship, the beauty of the world, music, the sky at night, the colours of the rainbow. And it's all free, Fionn; all of it."

"And what about this destiny that we are all born with?"

"Well, each one of us is unique. There is no one else like you in the entire world; there never was, and there never will be again. And the reason we are unique, and the reason we were born into this world when we were, is because we have been sent to do something very, very special with our life."

"Each and every one of us is here for a reason. It would, of course, be much easier for us to live a happy life free from mistakes if someone told us on the day we were born what our destiny actually was to be. Since we have forgotten the secret of our destiny, we have to live each day with emotional courage, making the best choices we can make in order to live life to the fullest possibilities that we have been given. The biggest sin in life is to waste the talents we have been given, to ignore the possibilities of who we were born to become."

Fionn's energy seemed to be coming back to him a little, "What do you mean by saying 'we have forgotten the secret of our destiny'?"

"Well, Fionn, some people believe that before we were born, our Soul knew the secret of our destiny. And that, in fact, our Soul actually chooses the parents and the family we wanted to be born into so, that we would have the best possibility of achieving the full potential of our destiny."

"That sounds a bit strange to me," said Fionn. "How do you explain children choosing to be born into lives of poverty and starvation, or being born to parents who hurt, or abuse, or abandon them?"

"I know it does sound a bit strange, but the idea is that a child born into a very poor family might have the type of life where they decide they are going to become a politician and change the world, so that no one else has to live in hunger, or without heat, or a place to call their own home. The choices we make in life are very important. If leaders in the world made different choices, no one would have to be hungry or homeless, do you know that?"

"Yes."

"Or, if at times of fear of war, our leaders could speak with healing words, instead of fighting words, we would not need to go to war or fight and die for our beliefs. All beliefs matter and hold some of the

The Wisdom of Your Name

~e~

"The wisdom of my name?"

"In olden times, before a child was born, the elder of a clan or village would perform a very special ritual where he would listen very, very carefully to the voice of the unborn child. The elder would ask the baby, 'what is it you are being born to achieve in this world?' And he would wait for the Soul of the child to answer from within the mother's womb. The voice of the child often spoke from the mouth of the mother, but it was never the mother speaking; it was always the Soul of the child. For no one else can ever tell you the destiny of your life, not even your mother."

"And what has that got to do with my name?"

"Oh yes, well, once the elder had listened very carefully to the voice of the unborn child, the elder would choose a name that held the secret of who you were born to become. All names mean something; for example Caelum means *Heaven Sent* and Lorcan means *Little Fierce One*."

"What does Fionn mean?"

"Fionn means *fair*: fair of hair, and fair in judgement. The secret of your name is that you are the *Fair One*. Born of Muirne and Uail, you were born to be the true Chief of the Fianna of Ireland. You cannot deny the destiny of who you were born to become. The woman you are searching for - your mother - is Muirne, and she lives with the King of Kerry. That is the secret of your name; the destiny of your birth."

"And tell me, please, how can I find my mother and my stepfather, now that I know who I am searching for?"

"Follow your true path. It can lead to only one place."

Then Fionn remembered how tired he was, "I am so weak, my body is spent, my energy has left me, that is why I am here now. That is how I came to fall to my centre, as you say. I have nothing left to offer."

The Tramp shook her head, "Fionn, be careful of what you say. You have lost energy only because you have struggled long and hard. You are tired and that makes sense. But you have nothing left to give only because you have lost faith in yourself. That is one of the greatest sins of all. God has given you a body that is the temple of your Soul in this world. Do not disrespect your body. Give it the love and positive energy it deserves. Negative thoughts create negative energy; to think yourself down pulls your mood and energy down. Think how you want to be. Think positively, and the outcome will be positive. Love the body you have been given, praise God, and never lose faith in yourself. Always believe in yourself. Always believe in yourself."

Fionn felt as though the Tramp was now preaching too much to him, almost talking down at him. "If you do not mind me saying so," Fionn replied, "it strikes me that you have not respected the body that God has given to you. You look as though you have spent a life abusing your body, maybe drinking too much, or living rough, never committing to company, friendship, or even good shelter. It looks to me as though you have wasted what you have been given by God."

"Indeed, Fionn, your eyes do not mistake you, but I simply remind you of what your Aunts once taught you: God's Angels appear in many mysterious ways. Everyone you meet has something to tell you, even the tramp on the street."

Fionn thought to himself of all the wisdom and strength the tramp had imparted to him during the few minutes of their conversation. He felt terrible for misjudging her and disrespecting her.

"How can I thank you for all you have given to me? Tell me what should I give to you in repayment?"

The Tramp smiled a most wonderful smile, "Fionn, when you treat the world and its people with love and respect, you owe it nothing. When you live your life with an open heart and spread the love of God within your heart, the world will provide you with all you ever need; not what you might want, but always, without fail, what you need. Do you know how many people pass a tramp each day without giving them even a penny? Today, you have given me time, and company, and conversation. You have shared with me some of the greatest gifts within our power to give. I thank you for these gifts."

Fionn and the Tramp smiled to each other.

"Do you see me now?" asked the Tramp.

"Yes" said Fionn, "I see you, and I thank you."

Two Roads

~e2~

Fionn looked about him, searching into the wonders of the world once again. This time, he saw two roads diverge in front of him. At the beginning, both paths looked much the same, but looking into the future, as far as he could, Fionn realised that each path would in fact bring him on a very different journey. However he could not see so far into the future as to tell if each path would in fact lead to a different place and time. One of the paths looked a little bit familiar to Fionn. It looked more comfortable than the other; the markings and signs looked as if he had been there before. It seemed to Fionn as if this path was more even underfoot. This path looked more worn to Fionn - even though the evening's light was now turning and, in the shadows cast, Fionn could not be exactly sure of what he thought his eyes could see.

The other path looked more challenging in the shock of its newness. The climb seemed steeper, with more shadows and shades. This path seemed more uneven underfoot. With a few more twists and turns, this path climbed to a point, and then seemed to travel into a future that Fionn could not see or predict. The signs were unusual, and they all pointed to something new and different. And the ground underfoot was far less assured to Fionn. This road would carry many risks and challenges, but with it also the possibility of something new, something greater. Fionn sat and measured his choice. He knew he was facing a time when he would have to face a decision, a time when he would have to confront the pain of who he was born to be.

He thought to himself, 'This is the type of emotional pain you can't go around, or over, or under. It is the type of pain in life that all you can do is go through. Only in going through these pains can you learn the lessons and come out the other side a different and better person.'

Fionn knew he must do one of three things: he must make a decision, stay where he was, or go backwards. He also knew that he was facing one of those moments that really mattered in life, but what was he to do?

The three fears - making a decision, making the wrong decision, or making no decision - seemed to keep Fionn rooted to the spot in doubt. More than this, once he realised he was stuck in the moment, he began to panic. He knew that panic and fear always went together to cause the wrong decision. The image of the beautiful kind woman that Fionn had first seen as the old Tramp, in the Fifth Province, had disappeared; lost in the changing light. But the wisdom of her voice remained strong and, when Fionn spoke to her, she answered.

"Two roads diverge," Fionn wondered, "Which one should I follow?"

The beautiful woman spoke to him, "'Should' is the wrong word. Others can tell you what they believe you should do, but only you can decide which road is the right road to take in life."

"But I find it so hard to choose," replied Fionn. "To take one means missing out on the other. What if I make the wrong choice?"

"You, already know that this is very important choice in your life. One road is your Soul's Path; the other is a distraction. One will bring you to your Heart's desire; the other brings struggle and unhappiness."

"Yes and that choice has me frozen here waiting for advice."

"Ah," replied the beautiful woman. "At times like this, when you are faced with such momentous life changing choices, you can not take advice. You can only make a decision, and follow that path."

"How will I know if I am right?"

"Your heart will know."

"And if I am wrong?"

"If you are wrong, you can always make another decision. You are never free from making choices in this life, never."

Just at that moment, somewhere overhead, Fionn heard the cry of a curlew. He remembered a saying his Aunts used to say: 'When you hear the curlew cry, Angels are close by.' Fionn closed his eyes again, and began to pray.

When he opened his eyes again, he saw a huge white Stag standing in the clearing, some way down one of the two paths. The Stag was majestic and still. It reminded him of his Guardian Angel, someone he had not thought of in a very long time. He remembered the voices of his Aunts, "Your Guardian Angel is always with you, and takes many forms and shapes, if only you have the eyes to see and the ears to hear."

Fionn stood up and began to journey onwards in his life once again. He knew which path to follow.

Finding His Mother and Stepfather

~e2~

It wasn't long before the path he had chosen led him to his birth mother, Muirne, and his stepfather, the King of Kerry - as he knew in his Heart it would.

Fionn was amazed by the time he shared in the company of his birth mother and the man that could have been his stepfather. Having grown up in the care of his Aunts, he had always been unsure what his relationship with his mother might actually be like. And for all this uncertainty, he had never imagined what his life might have been like if he had ever had the chance to experience the true love of a stepfather.

Fionn grew to resent his mother, even more than he thought ever possible. He always felt he carried the wound of an absent parent - the wound the Temper Monster spoke of in the depths of the forest. But now that Fionn spent time with the King of Kerry, he resented his mother for having denied him the experience of the healing power of a man's love; the love that he believed in his Heart the King of Kerry could have offered to him as a stepfather.

Having grown up in the care of his Aunts, Fionn knew so well that true parental love did not depend upon a birth right, or blood inheritance, alone. But could be developed, and worked on. True love took time, and emotional investment, sharing time listening to what the other person doesn't say as well as what they do. True love is the great reward for the hard work of hands-on care and the simple spending time with someone. Beginning there in the hard times: facing up to the responsibilities of a relationship, staying with someone in the difficult times; the giving as well as the giving out to someone else.

This love involved a risk as well as a reward and, sometimes, as Fionn well knew, birth parents were not the only, or even the best, people to give this love to a child. But for all the realisation of the sadness of this loss, Fionn's birth mother held the answer to a secret that nobody else in the whole world possibly could: the story of the truth as to why she really gave Fionn into the care of his Aunts on the occasion of the death of his father.

Fionn had spent his whole life arriving at this moment; he was not going to shy away from the difficult question, and so he asked,

"Why, mother, did you ever give me up? Why was it that you did not keep me with you? Why did you choose to give me over to the care of my Aunts?"

Some might think that Fionn's mother might have been afraid of the question; many thought her own life had protected her from the honesty of this very same question. But instead of being afraid of the question, the question seemed to set Muirne free from the terror of the past that held her captive too.

Muirne looked into his eyes, "If the truth were told Fionn, there were many reasons, not just one. At the time, I did not have the confidence within me that, I believed, a new mother needed in order to give her child the right care and love in life. I was afraid I was not good enough to be your mother and, in my fear, I had no one close enough to give me the advice or support that might have made a difference; for that, I am eternally sad. In their place, though, I had many powerful people who gave me advice that I should give you over to the safe care of others. They worried that, without your father's support, I would not be able to offer you the true care and protection you would need in this life. Their advice was so strong, that I would never be good enough, and so I gave you up to the care and protection of your Aunts.

Not for the first time in his life, Fionn began to see another side to someone he had come to judge and see under just one light. He found himself warming to his mother, pitying her almost, feeling something new within himself for the story of who she was. Fionn held the woman who had given birth and life to him in his arms. He was almost a man now and his arms and Heart were strong. She cried in his arms; she wept like a lost child. Fionn cried for her, and the child she had lost.

In the evening time, Fionn got to know the man who might have been his stepfather. The care and love of another man was something quite new to Fionn. The type of hands-on care work that true men were capable of was something that Fionn had never experienced previously.

When Fionn was tired, this man made a bed ready for him. When he was hungry, the man made food more beautiful and satisfying than any Fionn had ever tasted before. When Fionn felt upset, the man seemed to have time to listen and words to comfort. It was as though he knew the healing power of words and company. And when he held Fionn in a hug, it felt safe and true. When Fionn cried, it was with love, rather than sadness. Fionn thought to himself how tears tasted differently depending on the emotions behind them.

By the time he met the King of Kerry, the man who could have been his step-father, Fionn had grown strong in body, and quick with speed. He knew the beauty in the rhythm of Nature, and had grown to know when he needed to make choices and follow the difficult path in life. Fionn was well on the way to becoming a fully-skilled Emotional Warrior.

Fionn's stepfather, knowing how fully developed Fionn already was, began to teach him how to think, quickly and with foresight. He began to teach Fionn how to trust his intuition by teaching him the skill of playing chess, and, being a sharp learner, it was not long before Fionn could beat his stepfather in every game.

His stepfather spoke more than anyone else had ever spoken together with Fionn. In turn Fionn found it easier to speak from his Heart in the company of this man, than with anybody he ever had before. And so, Fionn asked to speak with him about truth.

The Usefulness of Truth

~e2~

F ionn began the conversation, "I have come all this way in my life in the search of the truth of the story of who I was born to be: the truth of my birth."

His stepfather seemed to take a moment before speaking, as if checking with himself whether Fionn was ready for the answer, "Fionn, truth can be a very strange thing. You need to be careful in life for the truth that you ask after. You need to be ready to hear the truth before you can ever ask to be told the truth."

"I asked my birth mother the truth of why she gave me over to the care of others when I was born. She told me two sides of the story - that she feared she could not give me the love and care I deserved, and that others, more powerful than her, strongly advised her to give me over, since they did not believe she could provide the care and protection I would need in life. But I have also heard another story why she gave me up. Some people say she fell in love with you, and they say, when a woman falls in love with a second husband, they often grow to hate all that belongs to the first."

There was a gentleness in his stepfather's words, "Fionn, the truth, like all stories, has many different sides. The real truth is most often found somewhere in the middle and never at the extremes."

"So many lies have been told about my mother, my birth, and why I came to live in the care of someone other than her. I seem to have lived all my life in search of a story that fits who I feel I really am."

"Fionn – what I am about to teach you, is something many of the wisest and most important people in this land have yet to learn. You are able to learn this lesson only because you are ready."

"Many people fear lies. Yet, one lie told against someone has no real power. Lies never last very long, because they have nothing to catch hold of. They hold no glimpse of truth. So even the biggest lie soon dies; when a lie is told about you, those closest to you, never doubt the truth, they simply know the truth of the person you are. The lie has no strength or power in the company of the dignity of your life."

Fionn's stepfather continued, "Much more dangerous, however, is the telling of a half-truth. Half-truths are much more damaging to a person's character, they hold enough of the truth to catch hold and take over. Enough of the truth even to cause your closest friends to begin to doubt your honesty and integrity."

"The most dangerous half-truth which can be told is the one that takes away the good name of another person. Such a curse can last for generations, being passed from father to son, or mother to son, as is your family's case."

"One of the greatest poverties in life is not having the power to have your own voice heard in the telling of the story of who you really are. One of the greatest injustices one man can do to another is to abuse his power by taking away the other's story telling rights. The Seanachaís knew that this was the most powerful curse that can be put on another."

Fionn felt a sadness. "How has my life been cursed in this way?"

"Well, the story of your mother was cursed in half-truths and rumours, Fionn. People have told half-truths about you, about your mother; each one taking away her good name and her story telling rights. Not only has she been damaged in all of this but, so too, you have suffered never knowing the full truth of who you were born to be."

"Father, I have been searching for a story of truth for a very long time; the truth of the story of who I was born to be. I thought that, in finding my birth mother, I would also find the comfort of the truth of who I was born to be? But I still feel unsure."

"Son, understanding the story of who you were born to be is only part of the journey in life. You also need to discover the story of who you are, and we all deserve to realise the story of who we dream we will become. So many people fear this possibility of becoming who they dream to be more than they fear the eternity of staying stuck in a way of life that does not make them fully happy. They choose the safety of staying settled where they are in life, of never really living life to the fullest possibilities and potential."

Fionn and his stepfather grew very close to one another, sharing time and conversations together in this way. However, by the time Fionn could beat his father at chess seven times in a row, his mother had become uncomfortable in his company. Some say it was because she once again feared for Fionn's safety and that the clan-Morna may have discovered that Fionn was now living in her home again. Others said it was because she was jealous of the time the two men spent together. It was soon after that his mother told him that he must leave. And so Fionn left home again, not for the first time, but for the last - on his journey to discover the truth of who he was born to be.

SAMHAIN
The Search for the Truth of Who You will Become

~e2~

Fionn's journey now seemed somewhat easier, his step seemed lighter. It was as if now, knowing the story of who he was born to be, he could go forwards in life knowing with a greater confidence that he would someday find the truth of who he would become.

Fionn soon came upon one of the legendary rivers of Ireland - one of the sacred streams whose waters flow upwards. Again, Fionn knew that this was a special sign; the type of sign sent from the Other World; the place of Fairies, and Angels; a sign from God himself. Fionn followed the winding path of the shoreline. As he walked, he gave praise to God in thanks for the constant presence of the earth.

With every footstep he took, Fionn could feel the crunch of the sand and stones of the shoreline underfoot. God had never left Fionn down - the World always came to meet, and greet, and support each and every footstep he ever took in life. Fionn looked around him, feeling the chill wind close around him in the night.

Fionn knew that, for all the bare nakedness of winter, the springtime would soon again follow, and with it would come new beginnings.

Fionn smiled knowing the truth of time and place.

Fionn followed along the path of the water's edge. It seemed to him that the shape of the shoreline was always changing, as if the water lifted part of the coast from here and brought it to rest somewhere else. Even in this natural chaos, Fionn was amazed by how little time nature needed to catch hold and start all over again.

As he walked together with the shoreline, with the wind in his hair and the sand and stones underfoot, Fionn had a deep feeling again of really being connected with the World around him. It was as if, in a strange way, the water and stones and wind and himself were all so connected, each was in fact part of the other. It was as if they could think and feel and dream together and know what each part was whispering to the other.

As he walked along the shoreline, Fionn listened more carefully to the voice of the earth and the wind. As the sands moved under his feet, it sounded to Fionn as if the earth was speaking to him. With every footstep he took, Fionn heard the world whisper out loud the word Hope. Each and every time Fionn took a step in the world, the crunch of the Earth beneath him spoke: "Hope, Hope, Hope."

It was a soothing, comforting chant that carried Fionn deeper into the night. The word brought strength and confidence for the journey, and, again, Fionn gave thanks to his God.

As he walked on, Fionn began to notice the change in the weather. Winter was now approaching and, with it, the world seemed colder, laid bare. White snow fell, covering the earth's secrets, as if letting the world itself sleep and recover its spiritual energy for the times that were to come.

The wind blew colder through the bare treetops and, as it whistled through the night sky, Fionn was sure it spoke another word. Now he heard the word Fear spoken on the wind: "Fear, Fear, Fear." The chill wind seemed to creep round behind him as he walked, whispering its warning from a dark and distant place.

Fionn stood still, caught between the twin voices of the earth and the wind.

Hope, Fear.

As he listened, Fionn realised that both of these words had accompanied every step he had ever taken. From the moment he had taken his first steps in the world in search of the story of who he was, the two words, 'Hope' and 'Fear,' had always been present.

In the middle distance, Fionn could see a light and, even though the night was dark and the wind was strong, the light burned constant and true. As Fionn looked towards the light, he began to see the shape of someone who suddenly seemed very magical indeed. It became difficult now for Fionn to make out if the light was actually coming from the person or not. Fionn got a strong feeling that this person was someone very special, as the figure reminded Fionn of some of the very special people he had met along the journey of his life. Even from this distance, Fionn had a warm feeling that he had met this person somewhere before.

Fionn began to walk again, towards the stranger - that he felt he knew - in the middle distance. As he did so, the voice of the earth and wind seemed to drift away, they became replaced with the crackling sound of the fire and the washing sound of the water.

The nearer Fionn came to the stranger, the stronger the noises became in his ears. The noises became almost deafening. Fionn again had to stop walking, trying to listen, trying to make sense of all that was going on about him, and inside of him too.

The noise of the fire became clearer, and, in the crackling of the flames, Fionn believed that once again he could hear the word: "Fear. Fear. Fear." It was as if he could not ever lose the voice of fear inside his head.

But so too, the voice of hope seemed eternally present; this time sung by the waves of water, each and every time they washed ashore. As though they were washing clean the land with every movement, they returned to the lake, leaving the stones on the shoreline sparkling, clean, polished, and full with the eternal promise of new beginnings.

Fionn walked on through the two voices of Fear and Hope. To journey in his life, he knew he would have to face both - you cannot have one without the other in this world.

Fear. Hope. Fear. Hope.

Even though he was growing tired, he found his energy was recharged. He felt as if he was being carried along by the changing rhythmical sounds of the earth and wind, fire and water. Fionn was drawn towards the constant light; it was as if it pulled him forward.

The promise of what might be was such that Fionn found courage to face his Fear and follow his Hope.

Meeting the Wise One

~e2~

As he approached the light, Fionn came to realise who the stranger before him actually was. Suddenly Fionn remembered the dream in which his mother visited him when he was six years old; the night she whispered the truth of who he was born to be. For legend had foretold that Fionn would meet one of the wisest poets in the land of Ireland, who would teach Fionn the beauty of words and the healing power of poetry.

Fionn recognised him as the Wise One he had been searching for.

When he spoke, it seemed as if Fionn had heard his voice before. It sounded like the voice of the Wise One at the Centre Within.

"You have arrived. You are welcome. I wondered how long you would remain stuck between the voices of Fear and Hope.

Fionn replied, "I have learned that when your Soul is scared, all you can do is make a choice. I have decided to follow my dream. That is how I came to arrive at this point in my life."

The wise one nodded, "How long have you travelled to arrive here?"

"All of my life," replied Fionn.

"And what is your dream?"

"To become the person I was born to be."

"Ah yes – you have arrived at a very good place in that case. Come, rest by the heat of the fire. You must be tired from your journey."

"I am tired from the struggles of my decisions, not from the journey itself," said Fionn.

"Indeed, but it is impossible to have one without the other, as you have learned. Your Aunts taught you to live your life in tune with Nature and the world of those around you. They taught you the importance of honour and love. The men you met on your journey taught you the dangers and delights of living life to its fullest potential. Your stepfather taught you the beauty of healing relationships, and to always question the usefulness of Truth. You have also learned that life cannot be lived without also experiencing the pain of loss and sadness at certain times. Here, I will teach you the beauty of words and the healing power of poetry."

"Why here, between fire and water?"

"Because, Fionn, you need both fire and water to live life to the fullest. Many men try to live life choosing only water. These men are calm and patient like the well, they try to be kind and gentle with others, but they can never be fully human since they need also to be able to touch the fiery, playfulness, and strength of fire. Some men choose to live life with fire alone. They are self-sufficient, bold, and carefree. But they, too, fail in life since they are too angry to allow others to ever come close enough to teach them how to love, and be loved in return.

Follow your Guiding Star

~e2~

That night, Fionn could not sleep, he tossed and turned untill at last he decided just to get out of his bed. Outside, the night sky lit up with the splendid light of a new moon. Fionn knew well from the past how hard it is to sleep when the moon is full. The stars that night seemed to dance and shine in a way that Fionn knew he had never really noticed before. Fionn walked into the night. The brightest star in the sky seemed to call him in a way he did not need to understand, but he followed it. The light led him to the shores edge and, there, he saw, the Wise One sitting facing his reflection in the still of the night's deep water.

The Wise One was fishing; he was not saying anything. He was still in the silence, lit up by the wonder of the starlight of the night. For the first time, Fionn noticed how small even the Wise One seemed to be under the exposure of the universe above. Fionn thought to himself that, all over the world tonight, the same moon and stars and sky looked over every single person. He wondered if he would ever understand the world - even if he lived to be a hundred.

Without turning around, the Wise One welcomed Fionn. It seemed he could hear Fionn's very thoughts.

"It is the same sky that looks over the whole world. We all sleep under the same moon, and live being warmed by the heat of the same sun, yet we spend our shared time finding differences between each other. Our skin colour, our faith, the type of food we eat, or whether we fall in love with men or women."

"Why do you think we spend our time looking at the differences between us?"

"Because Fionn, what we have in common is so simple and true, many of us are terrified of its beauty. We are all more alike than we are different. Each one of us has parts of ourselves that we do not like, so we try to imagine these parts of us as being something to do with someone else other than ourselves; then we can choose not to like, or accept, or love that other person. Do you understand?"

"I think so."

"We try to pretend to ourselves that we are good and others are bad. We do this by dividing the world into different halves, into differences."

"For example?" asked Fionn.

"Well, for example, the difference between young and old. The young think they are better than the old, since they have youth on their side. While the old think they are better, since they believe they have wisdom. And then there is the idea of nationality. We claim to be Irish, English, Australian, American or Middle Eastern so that we can trick ourselves into believing that we belong."

"But we all want to belong, don't we?"

"Yes, belonging brings a sense of comfort and safety that we all need from time to time. But when we say that others are not welcome to join us, it can only ever be a false sense of belonging - that is the terrible pity of nationality. True belonging belongs to the hearts of people; it is not dependent on geography, borders, religion, or language. It does not even belong to our history, it belongs to our future. True belonging begins with a feeling of love. Love is always welcoming. Love always sees what we share in common with others."

"But difference is all around us?"

"Yes, Fionn. We need difference in order to understand the world; without the dark, we could not see the light. Without the temptation of evil, we would not know the experience of good. Without times of pain and struggle, we would not appreciate the joy of success."

"I understand - but surely you do not mean to say that we should not try to do good rather than evil in life?"

"No, we must always try to do good with the life we have been given to live - that is all we are truly asked to do, to try to live a good life. Remember, as your Aunts taught you when you were young, 'do unto others as you would have them do unto you'."

"Yes, but then we must also have rules in life; how else then would we do the right thing? Without rules, how could all the people of the world actually share the earth, the plants, the animals, the wood, and the beauty of the world?"

"You are right, Fionn, the reason we have rules is so that we can try to get on together. That is why rules were originally made. Most rules - were created out of good intentions - to help us to share, to do good, not to hurt each other, but to look after the poor and the old - but it is not the only way. The difficulty is that, even when rules are made from good intentions, they can have bad effects! There is another way for all of us to live in this world and to be able to share - a better way."

"How is that?"

"It is quite simple - if we learned to trust ourselves. If we believed in ourselves, then we would have the confidence to believe and trust in others. If we believed others, we could trust each other to share together what each of us needs, not what each of us wants. We would no longer gather and hoard out of a fear of what we might need in the future. Fear of what we might be stops us from living with the truth of the present. Remember the other lesson your Aunts taught you - always believe in yourself! When you really believe in yourself, you have no need for fear in life. You can then trust others, and we can all share the beauty of the world. That is the only way we can all survive together. That is the real challenge for society."

"You will have to explain that some more to me."

"Well, think about it a bit - many of the world's best people live their lives trying very hard to keep a certain number of rules. Keeping rules, however, actually stops us from taking the risk to live life to the full. For example, some people live by the rule of living by day and sleeping by night. They fear what the night has kept secret, avoiding shadows or darkness, they try to keep to the safety of their warm beds. Just imagine all that you would have missed tonight if you choose to sleep instead of going out into the world at night to live.

"Yes, but tonight I did not choose not to sleep - I could not fall asleep!"

"That's the other part of it - there comes a time when we simply cannot keep to the rules anymore. It is as if the whole universe conspires to cause us to do the very thing we never would have chosen to do. Those moments - that can feel really frightening - when we feel the world we know and live in is falling apart on us - are actually very special moments for us. I call them *Magic Moments* - a moment when we choose one path in life over another, or when we take a risk and it pays off. At the time we are terrified but, when we look back on our life, we know we were guided to do the thing that was right for us. I am sure you can think of times in your life when you faced such life changing challenges?"

"Yes, I remember them."

"Well, not everyone takes these challenges, or faces up to the decisions we have to face in life. Some people freeze in front of things. They use the excuse of 'keeping the rules.' The real truth is that they are afraid of change so they never grow, learn, or develop. You can recognise them in your own life: they are the ones who talk about keeping on the straight and narrow path, keeping the rules."

Fionn and the Wise One slipped back into the quietness of fishing, being still in the moment, waiting for what the Universe would provide.

The Salmon of Knowledge

~e~

L egend has it that a Wise One would be found sitting by a pond of the river, which was surrounded by a copse wood of hazel trees. These trees grew nuts, which held within them all the wisdom of the world and as they fell from the tree into the pond, they were eaten by the Salmon of Knowledge: 'An Bradán Feasa.' Any man who ate of the flesh of this fish would possess all the knowledge of the world: knowledge of the past, the present, and the future. For seven years, the Wise One had tried to catch the Salmon of Knowledge but to no avail.

Fionn asked, "Why do you live by the river?"

To which the Wise One replied, "It is by water that the best poems are found."

And Fionn asked, "Have you caught many poems?"

To which the Wise One wisely replied, "Only those I have been fit for."

Just then the Salmon of Knowledge was caught.

Fionn knew he was sharing a very special moment with the Wise One. He could feel the warmth of success at the end of a long effort. The Wise One seemed to glow with a depth of satisfaction. He was delighted and tired from his efforts, and he asked Fionn to prepare and cook the fish for him while he rested. Fionn was delighted to be of help.

Fionn knew he was a good cook. As a child he had cooked for his Aunts and then on his journey and in times alone he had cooked for himself. As the Wise one left to rest, he turned back with a warning to

Fionn: "Whatever you do, young man, you must promise me you will not taste the flesh of the fish before me - for legend has it that he who tastes the fish first will receive all the wisdom of the world, the past, the present and the future.

Fionn, having always been an honourable man, made the promise with an open Heart as he said good night.

"I make this promise, with an open Heart - my word is my honour."

The Wise One smiled as he lay down to rest. "One of the most important gifts in this world is a man's ability to make a promise to another man," the Wise One whispered before falling asleep.

Fionn prepared the meal all night. He sat and kept careful watch as the fish roasted gently on the spit over the fire and by day break it was perfectly cooked. As Fionn took the fish from the fire, a red hot spark jumped up from the embers and burnt a tiny blister on the skin of the fish. Just as suddenly as the spark had surprised him, Fionn pushed his thumb into the blister to flatten the skin. With that, the heat of the fish oil burnt Fionn's hand so painfully that he thrust his thumb into his mouth for comfort.

When the Wise One awoke, he looked at Fionn and he knew Fionn had changed.

"You have tasted this fish," proclaimed the Wise One.

"No," said Fionn, "I gave you my word - I did not taste the flesh of the fish. I burnt my thumb and put it in my mouth."

The words were no sooner out of his mouth when Fionn realised the Truth of what had happened. Fionn was upset for the Wise One, but the Wise One did not become angry or resentful.

"You have not told a lie or broken your promise," he said to Fionn. "You spend the first part of your life making promises to others; the second part of your life trying to keep promises to yourself and the truth of who you really are. The truth is that you cannot deny your destiny, the person of whom you were born to become."

Legend has it that Fionn mac Cumhaill would be the one who would taste of the Salmon of Knowledge.

The Wise One smiled as he handed the fish to Fionn. Fionn smiled too, a smile from the very centre of his being.

The Centre of Who he had Become.

Suggestions for further reading

~e~

This story is a gathering of other stories. Like all stories the re-telling of this tale holds an echo of others' voices; authors, teachers, guides and friends I have been blessed to meet along the path. If you do not already know their work I would like to introduce you –

Ferguson, Harry., Hogan, Fergus., (2004), *Strengthening Families through Fathers*, The Department of Social and Family Affairs, Dublin.

Ferguson, Harry., Hogan, Fergus., (2007), *Men, Sexuality and Crisis Pregnancy*, Crisis Pregnancy Agency, Dublin.

Flaskas, Carmel., McCarthy, Imelda., Sheehan, Jim., (eds.) (2007), *Hope and Despair in Narrative and Family Therapy*, Routledge, London.

Malidoma Patrice Somé. (1994), *of Water and The Spirit*, Penguin, New York.

McCarthy, Imelda. (2002), *The Spirit of the Fifth Province: An Ancient Metaphor for a New Millenium*, in Feedback: Journal of the Family Therapy Association of Ireland. Vol 9. No. 2 PP, 10-13

Meade, Michael. (1993), Men and he Water of Life, Harper, San Francisco.

Moore, Thomas. (1992), *Care of the Soul*, Piatkus, London.

Moore, Thomas. (1997), *The Re-enchantment of Everyday Life*, Hodder and Stoughton, London.

Moriarty, John. (1994), *Dreamtime*, The Lilliput Press, Dublin.

Moriarty, John. (2005), *Invoking Ireland: Ailiu Iath N-Herend*, The Lilliput Press, Dublin.

O'Connor, Colm. (2015), *The Awakening: Living and Enchanted Life in a Disenchanted World*, Gill and Macmillan, Dublin.

O'Connor, Colm. (2013), *The Courage to Love*, Gill and Macmillan, Dublin.

O'Connor, Colm. (2010), *The Courage to be Happy*, Gill and Macmillan, Dublin.

Okri, Ben. (1997), *A Way of Being Free*, Phoenix House, London.

Okri, Ben. (1999), *Mental Fight: An Anti-spell or the 21st Century*, Phoenix House, London.

Sheehan, Jim. (1997), *Liberating Narrational Styles in Systemic Practice*, in Journal of Systemic Therapies. Vol. 18, No. 3, pp. 51 – 68.